la Cr...

& ...

Muffnut

Special thanks to
Gabi, Fona, Shanise, Anna & Marky for hoping for a happy ending.
SP!

The Cruffin and Muffnut published by Portmanteaux Picture Books.

10 9 8 7 6 5 4 3 2 1 ISBN: 978-0-9562117-4-3

First printing, April 2014. Printed in the UK by Mixam.

Written and illustrated by Alex Hahn.
Text and illustrations copyright © Alex Hahn 2014, all rights reserved.
Alex Hahn asserts his moral right to be identified as the
author/illustrator of the work.

Portmanteaux Picture Books is an imprint of Alex Hahn Publishing.
Visit: www.alexhahnpublishing.com | www.alexhahnillustrator.com

RAWR!

The CRUFFIN & MUFFNUT

ALEX HAHN

YOU HAVE
A LOVELY
ACCENT

--EEAYH?!

7.02 PM

WHEN SHE LAUGHS I CAN FEEL
MY HEART MELTING...

... SO, MAYBE ...

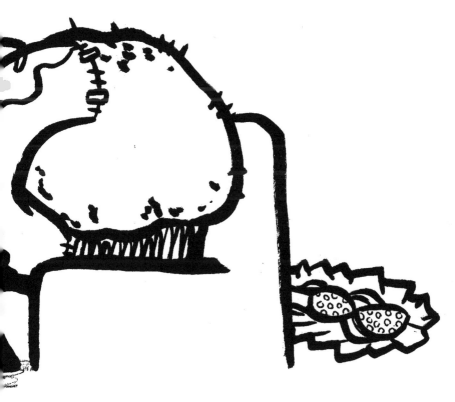

THAT CRUFFIN'S SMILE ALWAYS
BREAKS MY HEART

OW!

SORRY

YOU ALWAYS HURT THE ONE YOU LOVE?!

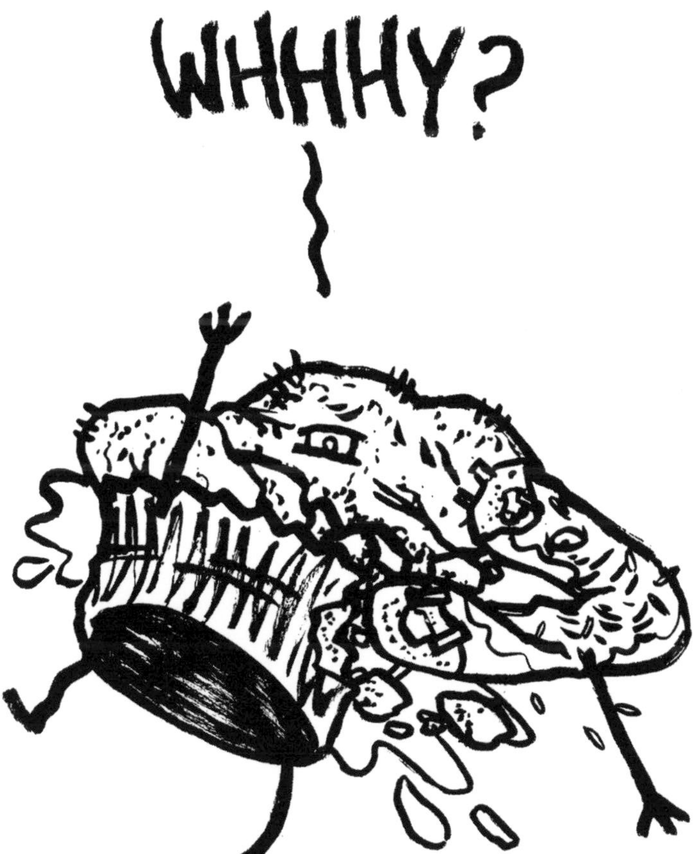
WHHHY?

AWAKE CRUFFIN

TIRED CRUFFIN

ALWAYS BEAUTIFUL!

EVERYBODY
HAS SOMEONE...

WHO CAN I TALK TO??

WOULD BE
THE WEEK MY
BEST FRIEND
IS...

... ELSEWHERE ...

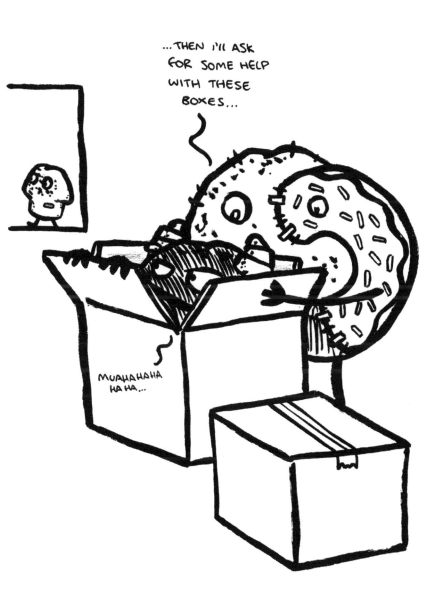

SIGH

I COMPLETELY RESPECT YOUR
FEELINGS - AND I'M SORRY IF YOU
REALLY AREN'T INTERESTED IN MY
AFFECTION - BUT PLEASE KNOW
THAT I DON'T JUST FEEL THIS WAY
ON A WHIM...

... WHEN I THINK OF US, I FEEL
LIKE I'M LOOKING AT THE FUTURE;

AND THE
FUTURE'S SWEET.

AND THEY
HAPPILY

ALL LIVED

EVER AFTER

...UNTIL